TITANS:
OLD FRIENDS

Judd Winick Writer

Ian Churchill Joe Benitez Julian Lopez Pencillers

Norm Rapmund Victor Llamas Andy Lanning Jon Sibal Prentis Rollins Bit
Sandra Hope Derek Fridolfs Joe Weems Oliver Nome Rodney Ramos Inkers

Edgar Delgado Colorist

Comicraft Travis Lanham Rob Clark Jr. Letterers

Dan DiDio Senior VP-Executive Editor **Eddie Berganza** **Elisabeth V. Gehrlein** **Dan DiDio** Editors-original series **Adam Schlagman** **Rex Ogle** Assistant Editors-original series
Anton Kawasaki Editor-collected edition **Robbin Brosterman** Senior Art Director **Louis Prandi** Art Director **Paul Levitz** President & Publisher **Georg Brewer** VP-Design & DC Direct Creative **Richard Bruning** Senior VP-Creative Director
Patrick Caldon Executive VP-Finance & Operations **Chris Caramalis** VP-Finance **John Cunningham** VP-Marketing **Terri Cunningham** VP-Managing Editor **Amy Genkins** Senior VP-Business & Legal Affairs **Alison Gill** VP-Manufacturing
David Hyde VP-Publicity **Hank Kanalz** VP-General Manager, WildStorm **Jim Lee** Editorial Director-WildStorm **Gregory Noveck** Senior VP-Creative Affairs **Sue Pohja** VP-Book Trade Sales **Steve Rotterdam** Senior VP-Sales & Marketing
Cheryl Rubin Senior VP-Brand Management **Alysse Soll** VP-Advertising & Custom Publishing **Jeff Trojan** VP-Business Development, DC Direct **Bob Wayne** VP-Sales

Cover art by **Ethan Van Sciver** with **Brad Anderson**

TITANS EAST SPECIAL #1
cover by Ian Churchill & Norm Rapmund with Rod Reis

THE FICKLE HAND, PART ONE:
GO EAST, YOUNG MAN
PENCILS BY IAN CHURCHILL
INKS BY NORM RAPMUND, ANDY LANNING & JON SIBAL

Y'KNOW, GANG, I GOTTA TELL YOU, THESE FELLAS WERE SOME SERIOUS HEAVY HITTERS.
BUT WHEN WE'RE TOGETHER, *NOTHING* CAN STOP US.
AND WE'RE *ALWAYS* GOING TO BE TOGETHER!
YOU GOT THAT RIGHT.
TITANS TOGETHER! TOGETHER FOREVER!
THAT WAS THEN.

THIS IS NOW.

OH... I'M SORRY. I JUST CAN'T COME.

HEY, YOU KNOW MY EVER CHANGING BRIGHT GREEN BUTT WOULD BE *RIGHT* THERE FOR YOU, BUT--

I'M ON ANOTHER TEAM, REMEMBER? MY HANDS ARE KIND OF FULL HERE.

I'D LIKE NOTHING BETTER... I WOULD... BUT--

NO.

I CAN'T. NOT NOW. EVEN FOR ME--

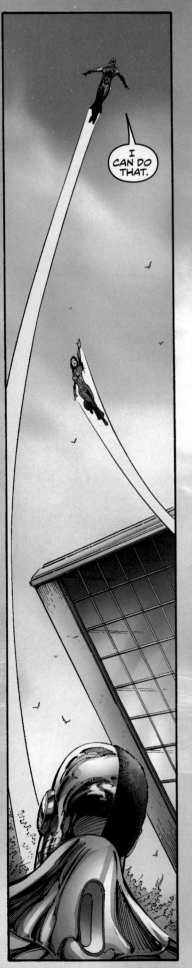

TZAAACK

TZAAACK

TZAAACK

TZAAACK

WHAT'S-- WHAT'S GOING ON?! REPORT!

TZAAACK

TZAAAC

REPORT! REPORT!

TZAAACK

DAMN IT TO HELL! WHAT'S GOING ON?! ANY OF YOU THERE?! WHAT'S--

OH NO... NO, NO, NO, NO...

TITANS #1
cover by Ian Churchill with Rod Reis

THE FICKLE HAND, PART TWO:
TODAY I SETTLE ALL FAMILY BUSINESS
PENCILS BY IAN CHURCHILL
INKS BY NORM RAPMUND

THE BAKER FAMILY HOME. SAN DIEGO.

HOME OF BUDDY BAKER, A.K.A. ANIMAL MAN.

AND ONE HOUSE GUEST.

I LOVE HOW MUCH THE BAKERS HAVE EMBRACED ME DURING MY VISIT, BUT...

KORIAND'R, A.K.A. STARFIRE.

IT IS NICE TO HAVE THE HOUSE COMPLETELY TO MYSELF... EVEN FOR JUST A LITTLE WHILE...

HUMAN PRUDISHNESS STILL BAFFLES ME. I WILL NEVER FULLY COMPREHEND HOW A SOCIETY THAT IS SO INTENSELY PREOCCUPIED WITH SEX IS EQUALLY COWED BY NUDITY.

I SUPPOSE IT IS MOSTLY THE UNITED STATES THAT GRAPPLES WITH THIS IRONY.

THE HEADQUARTERS OF THE DOOM PATROL.

I'M A GUY WHO CAN LEAD. I'VE FACED DOOM AND I CERTAINLY KNOW HOW TO PATROL.

THIS ALL MAKES ME ABUNDANTLY QUALIFIED TO LEAD THE DOOM PATROL, RIGHT?

BREEEEEEEEEEN

GARFIELD MARK LOGAN. BEAST BOY.

BUT, I APPARENTLY SUCK AT GIVING ORDERS.

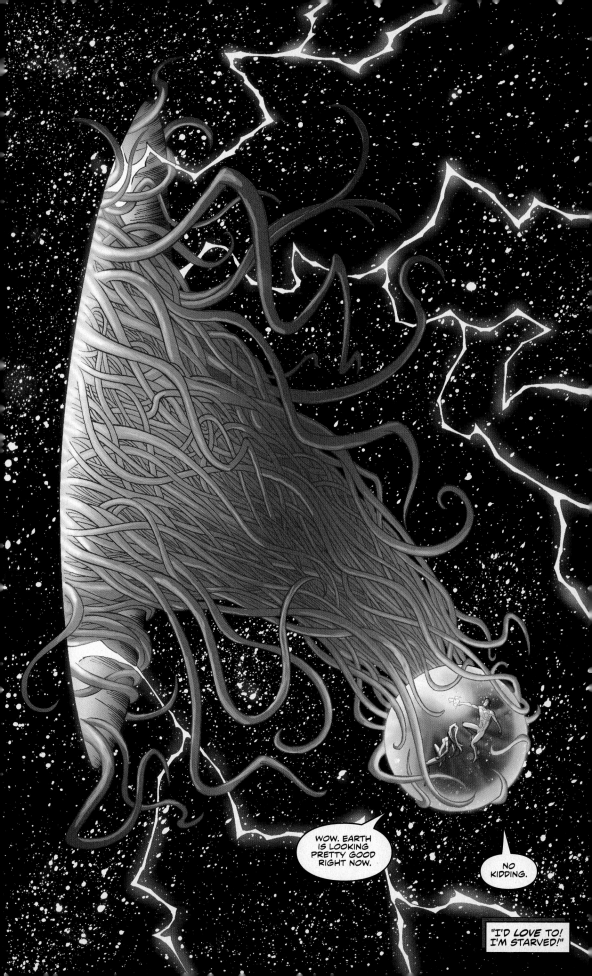

FAMILY AFFAIR, PART ONE:
ALL TOGETHER NOW
PENCILS BY JOE BENITEZ
INKS BY VICTOR LLAMAS

"WE'RE GETTING LOTS OF HELP."

"WHOEVER'S BEHIND IT."

YOU LOST A WAR? WITH WHO?

YOU WANT A LIST? A THOUSAND ARMIES HAVE TRUDGED THROUGH THIS PLANE, AND EVEN MORE OF MY MINIONS HAD BEEN SENT ELSEWHERE TO DO MY BIDDING.

I THINNED THE RANKS, THEN FOUND MYSELF ATTACKED FROM ALL FRONTS.

MY REALM, WHAT YOU SEE HERE, IS THE PHYSICAL EXTENSION OF MY METAPHYSICAL BEING. DESOLATE.

SO, YOU *REALLY* HAD YOUR ASS HANDED TO YOU.

ELOQUENTLY PUT. I HAD HEARD YOU'D COME TO ADOPT MORE OF HUMANITY'S LESS URBANE QUALITIES. IT'S QUITE DISGUSTING.

THAT COMING FROM THE FOUR EYED ANOREXIC DEMON BASKETBALL PLAYER.

FAMILY AFFAIR, PART TWO:
SINS OF THE FATHER

PENCILS BY JOE BENITEZ

INKS BY VICTOR LLAMAS, SANDRA HOPE, DEREK FRIDOLFS & JOE WEEMS

TITANS #4
cover by Ian Churchill & Norm Rapmund with Rod Reis

FAMILY AFFAIR, PART THREE:
DADDY'S LITTLE BOYS
PENCILS BY JOE BENITEZ
INKS BY VICTOR LLAMAS WITH OLIVER NOME

ARE YOU CERTAIN??

TITANS #5
cover by Joe Benitez & Oliver Nome with Edgar Delgado

I KNOW YOUR HEART
BECAUSE I KNOW MINE
PENCILS BY JULIAN LOPEZ
INKS BY PRENTIS ROLLINS & BIT WITH RODNEY RAMOS

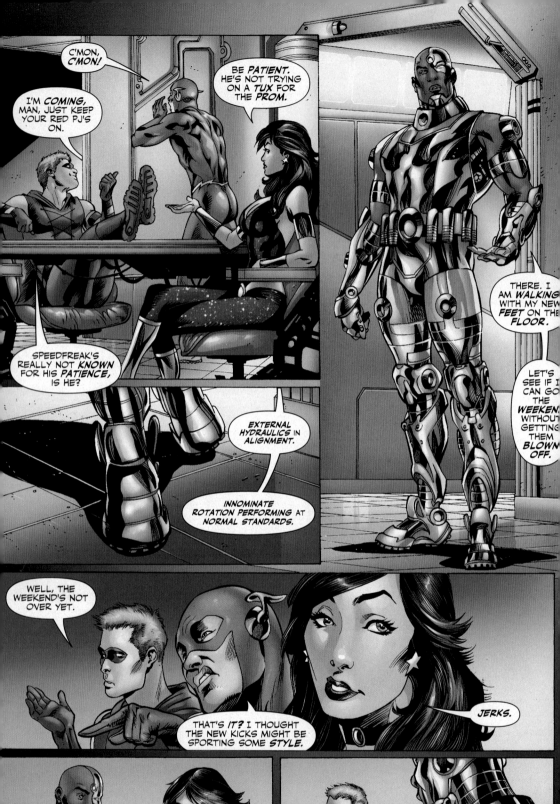

KORY...?

YOU'RE STAYING ON, RIGHT?

YES. I WILL STAY. I AM HOME WHEN I AM HERE.

KILL US? YOU WANT TO KILL US?!

NO! I THINK ABOUT IT... IT'S THERE--

WHAT THE HELL'S THAT MEAN? WHY WOULD YOU THINK SOMETHING LIKE THAT?!

BECAUSE I'M WRONG!!

DO YOU NOT SEE!? WE ALL PRETEND THAT I'M THE SAME AS ANYONE ELSE, THAT I HAVE THIS "DARK SIDE," BUT IT'S NOT A PROBLEM, BECAUSE I AM A GOOD PERSON AND I WANT TO DO GOOD!

I AM TELLING YOU-- I DON'T!

I'VE COME TO BELIEVE THAT MY TRUE SELF... THE THING I REALLY AM... ...IS EVIL.

THIS, MYSELF, RAVEN... IS JUST THE MASK IT WEARS. I AM THE THING IT USES TO HIDE FROM THE WORLD.

YOU DON'T HAVE TO *BELIEVE* US. BUT WE DON'T WANT TO *FIGHT* YOU, BEAST BOY.

I'LL ADMIT, WE'RE ALL PRETTY *PISSED* THAT WE GOT SCAMMED OUT OF STRIPPING OUR FATHER OF HIS POWERS, BUT THAT WASN'T *YOUR* FAULT.

WE JUST CAME TO GET OUR *SISTER.*

GET AWAY FROM--!!

WHICH PART OF "DON'T WANT TO FIGHT YOU" *DIDN'T* YOU UNDERSTAND?!

TITANS #6
cover by Joe Benitez & Victor Llamas with Edgar Delgado

TOGETHER. TOGETHER FOREVER

PENCILS BY JULIAN LOPEZ

INKS BY PRENTIS ROLLINS & BIT

PRIDE. AVARICE. ENVY. WRATH. LUST. GLUTTONY. SLOTH.

THE SEVEN "DEADLY" SINS.

AND *BELIEVE* ME, THERE IS *SIN* AMONG US. RIGHT ON EARTH. BUT *NOT* HOW YOU THINK.

WITH 6.6 *BILLION* HUMAN BEINGS LIVING ON THE PLANET, YOU *OF COURSE* IMAGINE THE AMOUNT OF VICE WOULD BE *ENORMOUS.* EVEN THE *MOST* PIOUS, THE MOST HOLY, OR JUST SIMPLY... THE *JUST*...

EVEN *THEY* WILL GIVE IN TO ACTS WHICH ARE PERCEIVED AS *INIQUITIES.*

BUT IT'S REALLY ABOUT *PERCEPTION.* NOT WHAT IS *RIGHT* AND WHAT IS *WRONG.* WHAT IS *NATURAL* OR WHAT IS *ABHORRENT.*

GOODNESS IS NOT THE *OPPOSITE* OF *EVIL. PLEASURE* IS *NOT* THE *OPPOSITE* OF *PAIN. LIFE* IS *NOT* A *BATTLE* WITH *DEATH.* THEY ARE ALL *PARTNERS.* THEY RUN *SIDE BY SIDE.* JOINED AT THE HIP. FIGHTING THE VERY *SAME* BATTLE.

DESPITE MY PENCHANT FOR *DARKER* COLOR SCHEMES, I DON'T SEE IT ALL SO *BLACK AND WHITE.*

"WE *HAVE TO*
FIND HER!!
NOW!!"

HANG ON...
YOU *FEEL* THAT?
I DON'T THINK
WE'RE *ALONE*
HERE.

SO MUCH
FOR THE ELEMENT
OF *SURPRISE!*

OH, I
DON'T KNOW,
FLASH...

...THEY
LOOK PRETTY
SURPRISED
TO ME!

"...I THINK IT'S JUST RAVEN!"

CAN'T SEE HER--

THE AIR IS GETTING HOT! WAY TOO HOT, AND THE GROUND IS--

GIVING WAY.

RAVEN! WHAT ARE YOU DOING TO US?!

I'M NOT DOING ANYTHING... EXCEPT...

I PLACED A SLIVER OF MY *PURE* ESSENCE WITHIN IT, THEN REMOVED ANY *MEMORY* I HAD OF DOING SO. THE *PLAN* WAS IF I WAS EVER *POSSESSED* BY MY EVIL SIDE AGAIN, THAT ESSENCE WOULD BECOME *SENTIENT.*

SO, YOUR *TRUE* SELF CAME TO LIFE IN THE GEM STONE AND FOUGHT BACK.

I LIKE TO *THINK* IT'S MY *TRUE* SELF. BUT THAT'S *DEBATABLE...* AND IT'S TIME I FACE SOME VERY *HARD* FACTS.

I CAN'T BE TRUSTED.

RAVEN--

NO. IT'S OKAY. I'M *NOT* SAYING THIS TO BE *MAUDLIN,* OR ACTING LIKE A *MARTYR.* I'M STATING A *FACT.*

THERE'S *EVIL* THAT RUNS THROUGH ME. AND WHEN THE WRONG SET OF *DEMONIC DUCKS* LINE UP, I HAVE A TENDENCY TO GO ALL *DARK DIVA* IN *THIGH HIGHS.*

BUT YOU SURE ARE *SOUNDING* A LOT MORE LIKE A *16-YEAR-OLD* AGAIN.

YES. Y'SEE, RAVEN, THAT'S A *GOOD* SIGN.

YOU'RE *COMPLETELY* YOURSELF AGAIN.

FOR NOW. BUT THERE MAY BE A TIME WHEN I GO OFF THE RESERVATION AGAIN.

THE RAMAT STONE WON'T WORK *TWICE.*

SO, I NEED YOU ALL TO TAKE *THESE.*

THEY'RE VARIOUS MAGICAL IMPLEMENTS AND TALISMANS.

WHAT ARE THEY FOR?

LOOK SHARP, EVERYONE! LET'S SEE WHO OUR UNINVITED *GUEST* MIGHT BE!

GOT 'IM!

MATCH!

WAIT-- WHO ARE WE DEALING WITH HERE?

HARD TO TELL. LAST WE LEFT OUR FRIEND HERE, HE REALLY WAS A "FRIEND."

DEFINITLY NOT THE END...